KASABIAN

DESIGN & ILLUSTRATION BY SIMON CORKIN
ARTWORK USED BY PERMISSION AND UNDER LICENSE FROM
SONY BMG MUSIC ENTERTAINMENT (UK) LTD

MUSIC ARRANGED BY ANDY JONES
MUSIC PROCESSED BY BASSLINE
EDITED BY LUCY HOLLIDAY AND MATT GATES
PRINTED IN ENGLAND BY CALIGRAVING LTD

ISBN 0-571-52489-3

TO BUY FABER MUSIC PUBLICATIONS OR TO FIND OUT ABOUT THE FULL RANGE OF TITLES AVAILABLE,
PLEASE CONTACT YOUR LOCAL MUSIC RETAILER OR FABER MUSIC SALES ENQUIRIES:

FABER MUSIC LTD, BURNT MILL, ELIZABETH WAY, HARLOW, CM20 2HX ENGLAND
TEL: +44 (0) 1279 82 89 82
FAX: +44 (0) 1279 82 89 83
sales@fabermusic.com
FABERMUSIC.COM

CLUB FOOT

Words and Music by Sergio Pizzorno and Christopher Karloff

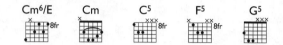

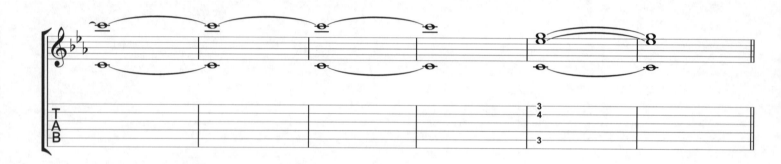

1. One, take con-trol__ of me, you're mess - in' with the e - ne - my. Said it's
2. Thrills take con-trol__ of me, stalk - in' 'cross the gal - le - ry. All these

12

PROCESSED BEATS

Words and Music by Sergio Pizzorno and Christopher Karloff

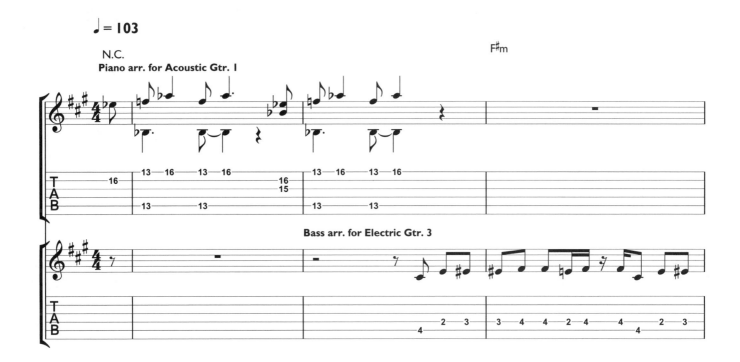

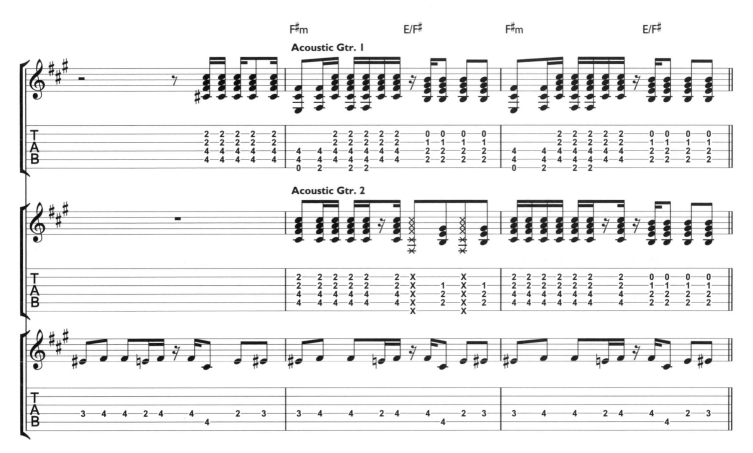

© 2004 EMI Music Publishing Ltd, London WC2H 0QY

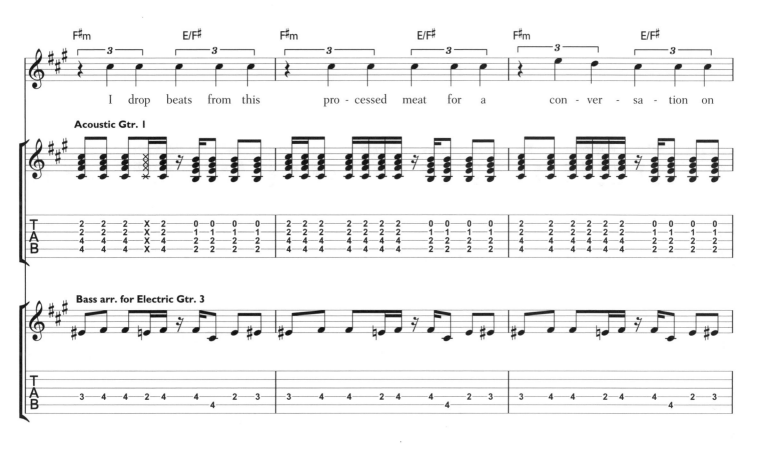

Lyrics: I drop beats from this pro - cessed meat for a con - ver - sa - tion on

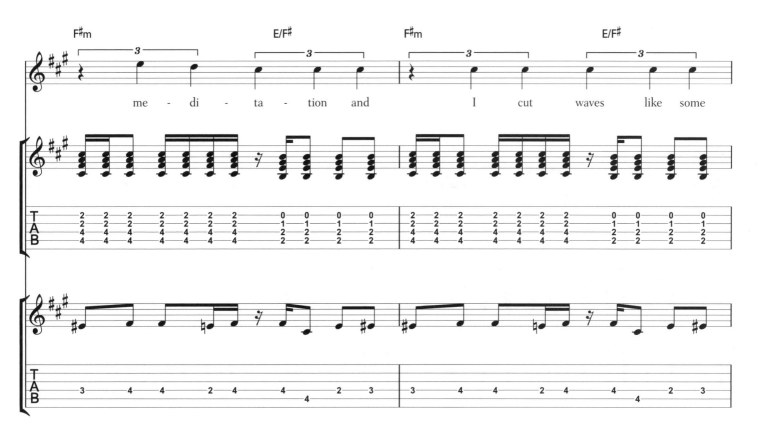

Lyrics: me - di - ta - tion and I cut waves like some

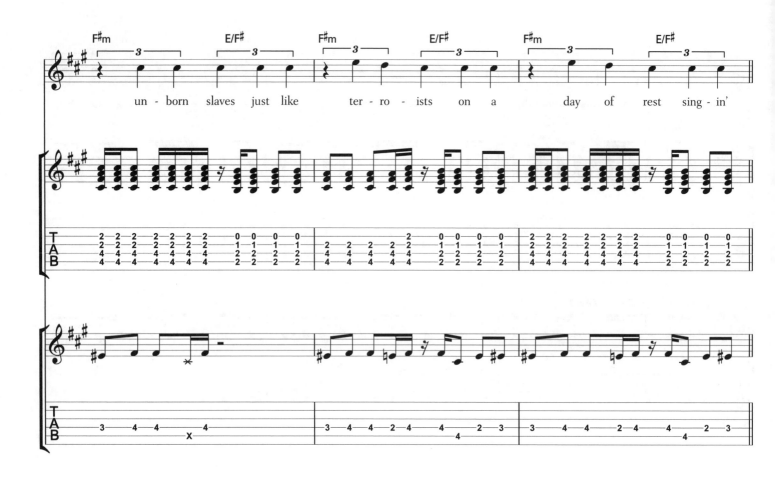

un - born slaves just like ter - ro - ists on a day of rest sing - in'

I _____ ran from the tide, _____ won't let you hide, _____ won't let you

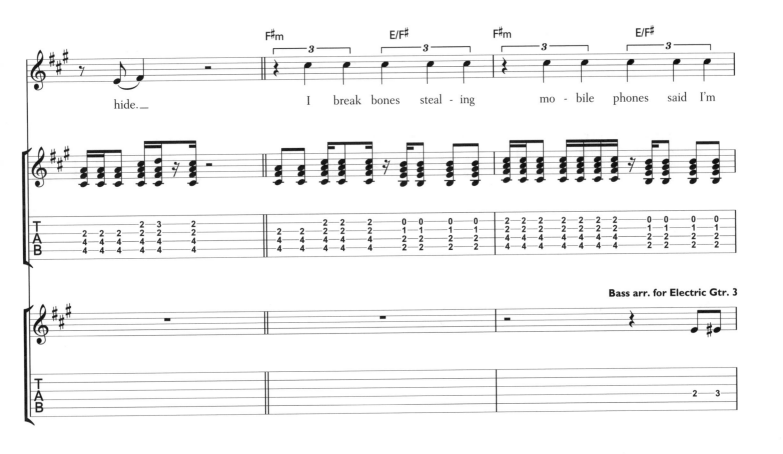

I break bones steal - ing mo - bile phones said I'm

Bass arr. for Electric Gtr. 3

cut - ting deals for these home - less meals, mak - ing id - le threats us - ing

Synth. arr. for Electric Gtr. 4

Synth. arr. for Electric Gtr. 3

allow delay effect to echo and fade

REASON IS TREASON

Words and Music by Sergio Pizzorno and Christopher Karloff

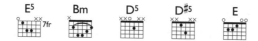

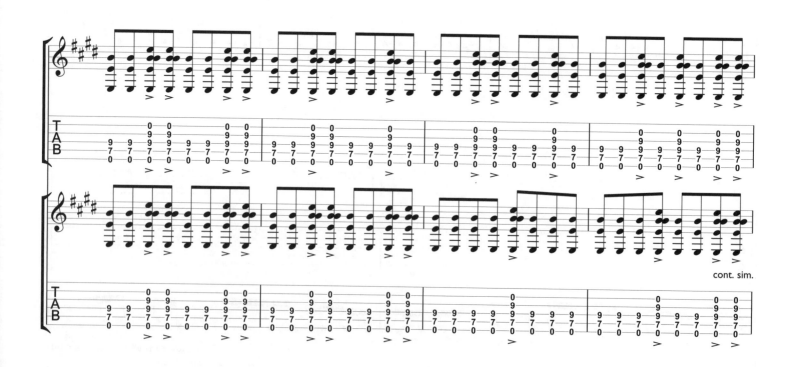

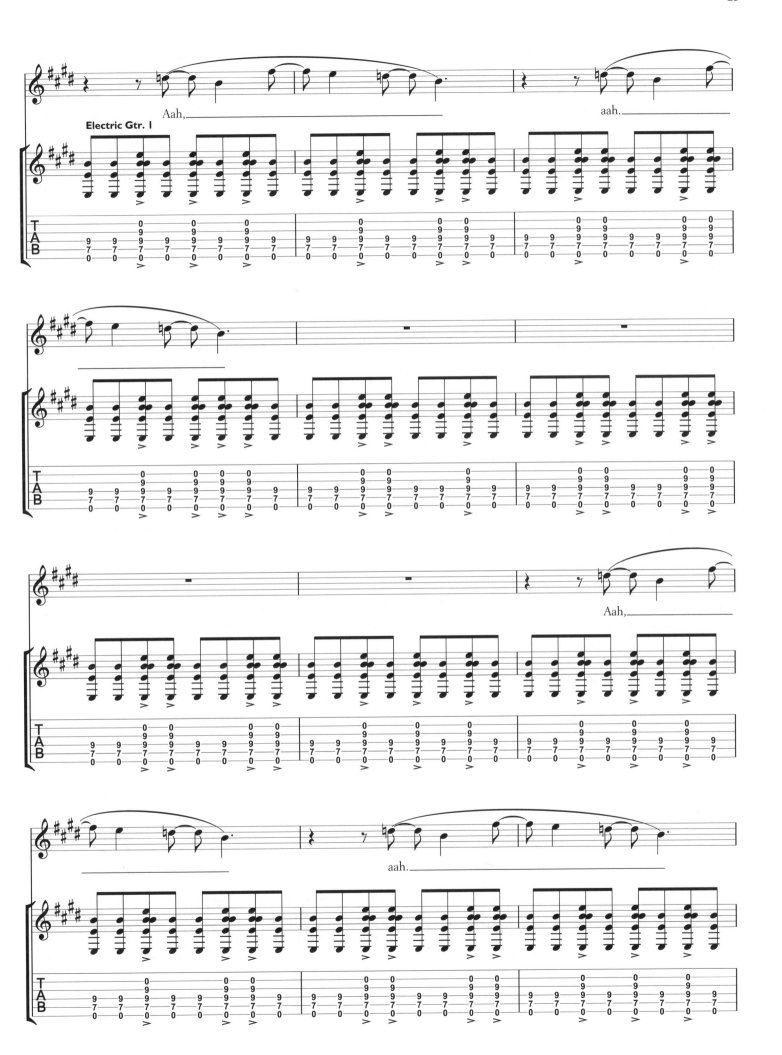

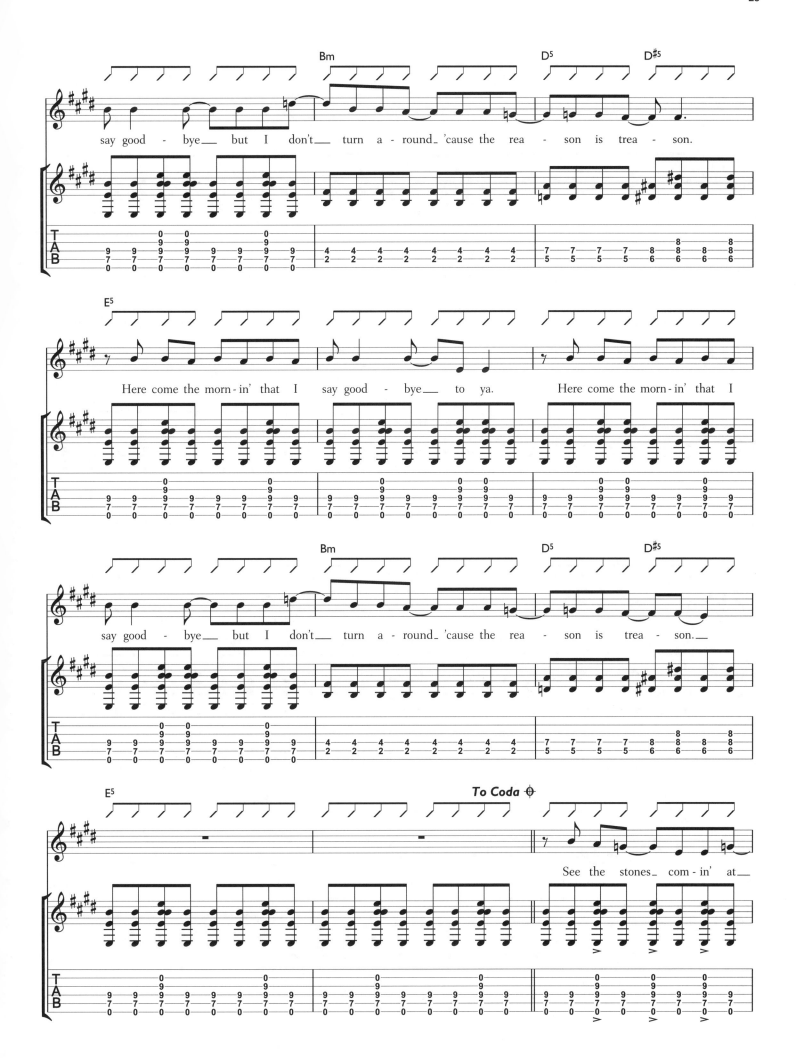

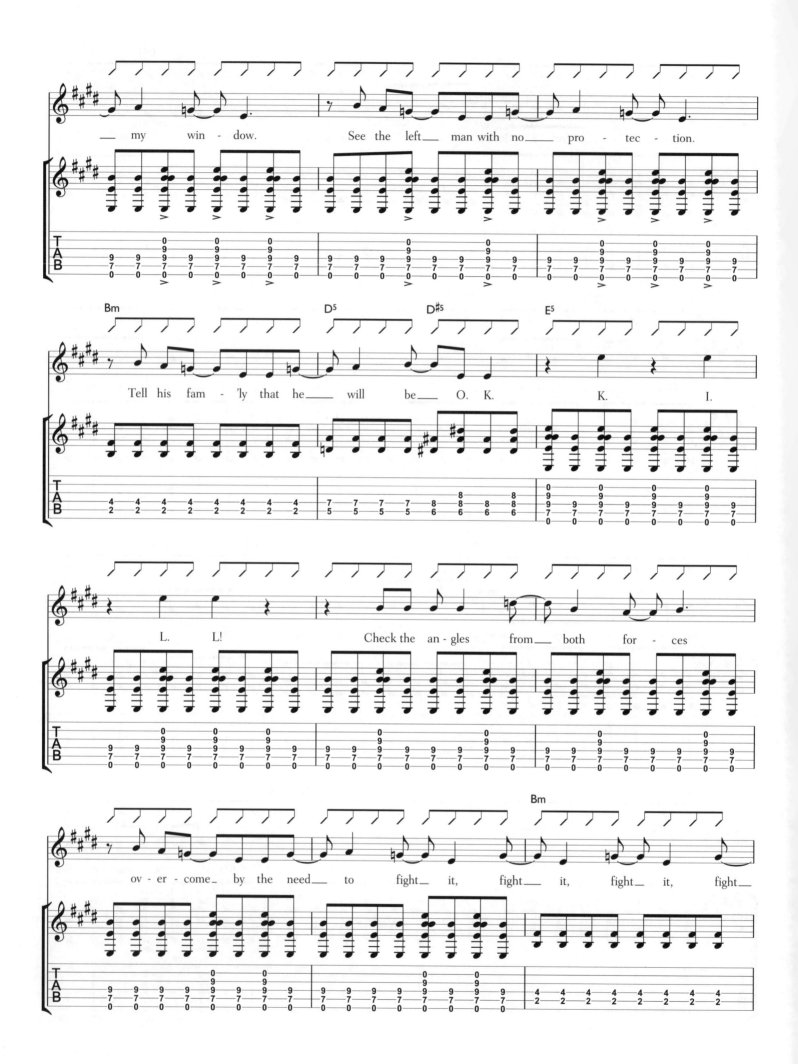

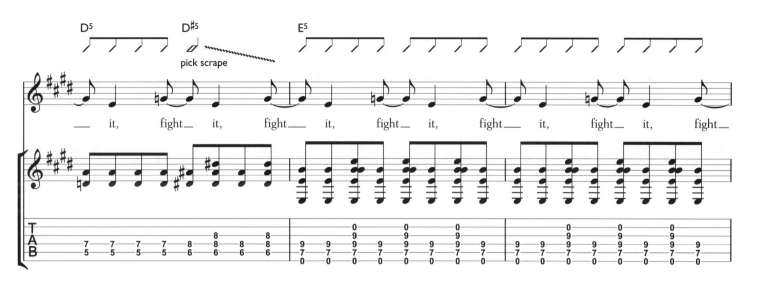

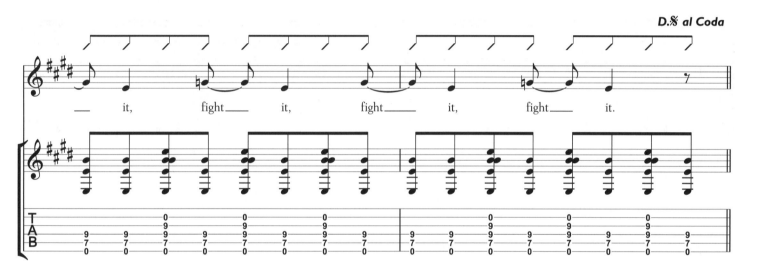

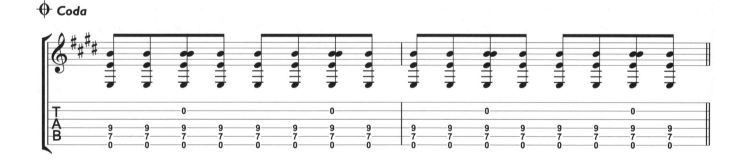

Synth. arr. for Electric Gtr. 3

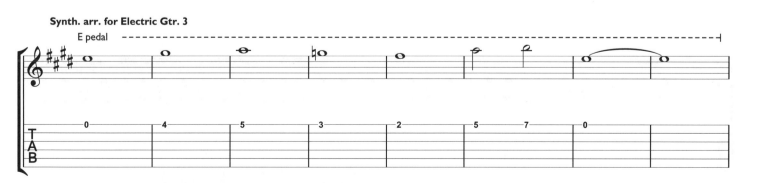

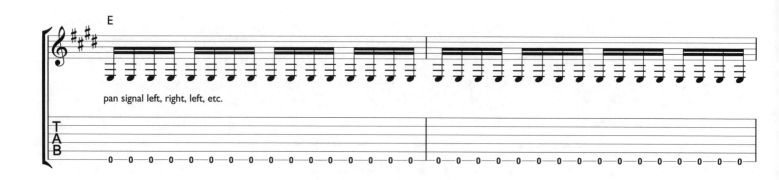

pan signal left, right, left, etc.

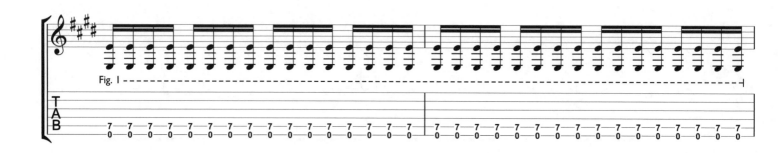

Fig. I

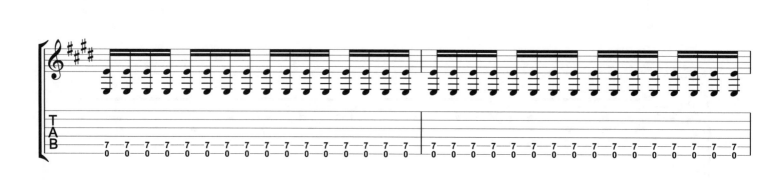

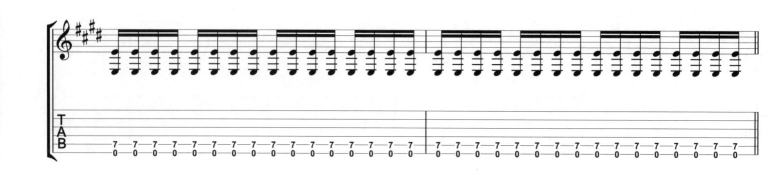

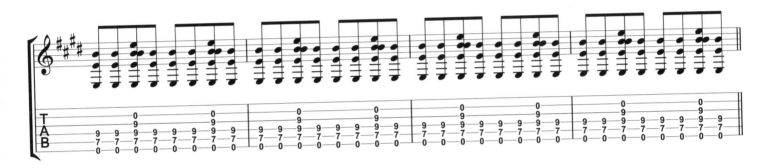

I hear the si-rens on___ the___ wall... I hear the

si-rens on___ the___ wall... I hear the si-rens on___ the___ wall...

I hear the si - rens on__ the__ wall... I hear the

si - rens on__ the__ wall... I hear the si - rens on__ the__ wall...

I hear the si - rens on__ the__ wall... I hear the

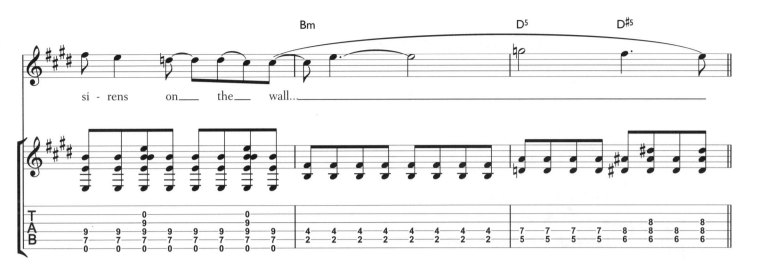

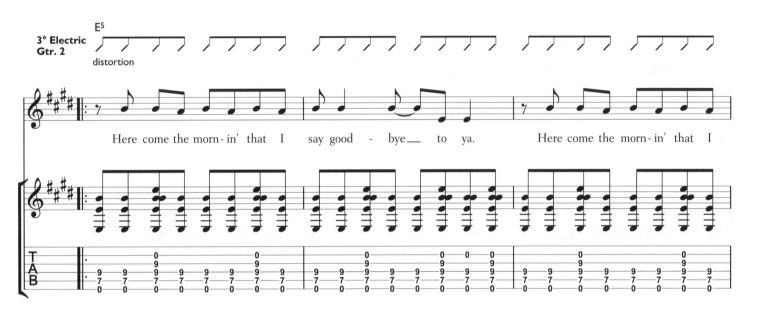

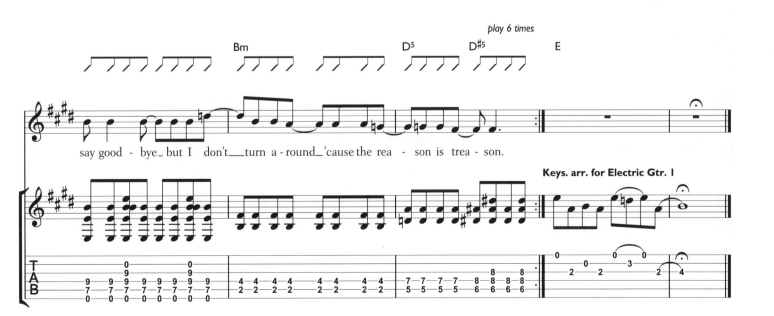

I.D.

Words and Music by Sergio Pizzorno and Christopher Karloff

♩ = 98

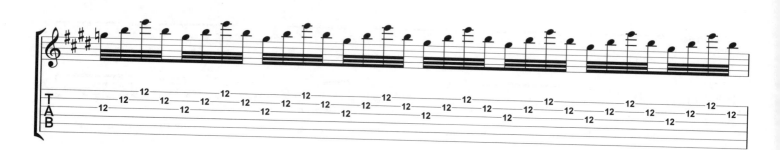

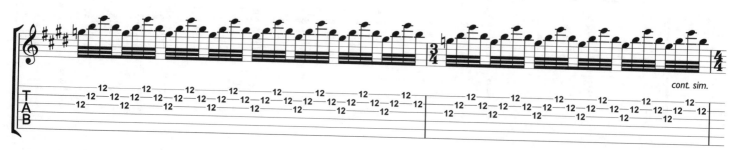

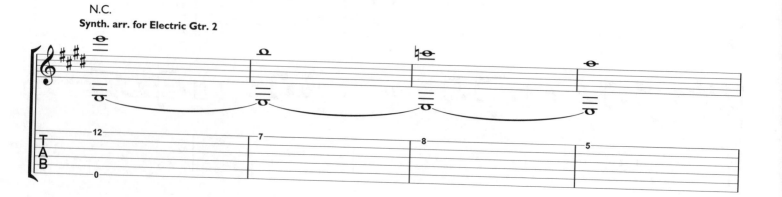

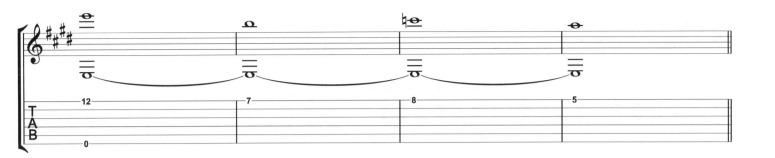

E   C

Synth. arr. for Electric Gtr. 2

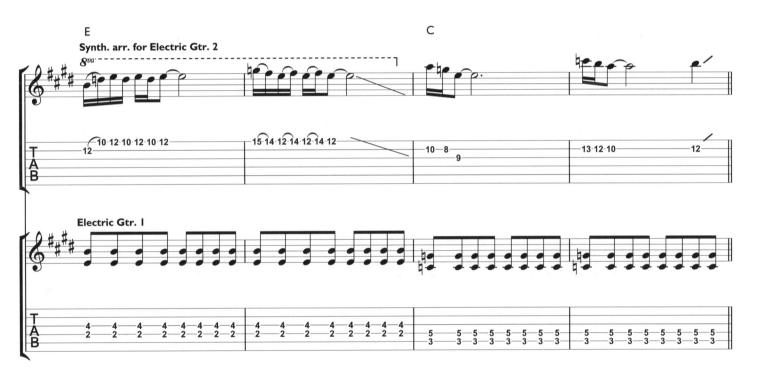

Electric Gtr. I

E   Cmaj⁷

No-one else_ is here,__ but I can't get_ a sense of no - thin'.

Electric Gtr. I

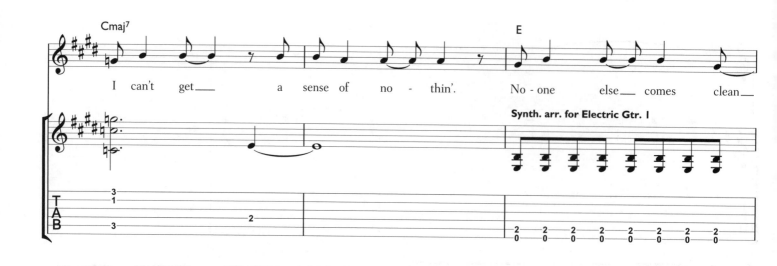

I can't get___ a sense of no - thin'. No - one else___ comes clean___

Synth. arr. for Electric Gtr. 1

___ but I can't sleep___ 'cause I got no - thin'.

Feel - in' I___ have lost___ con - trol to a high - er force and this

Synth. arr. for Electric Gtr. 2

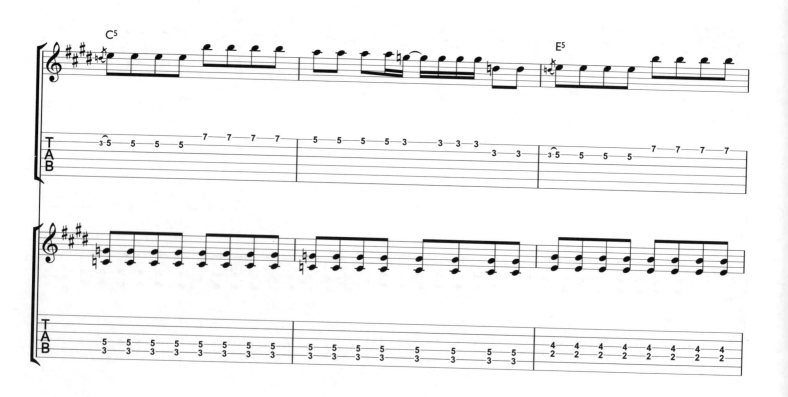

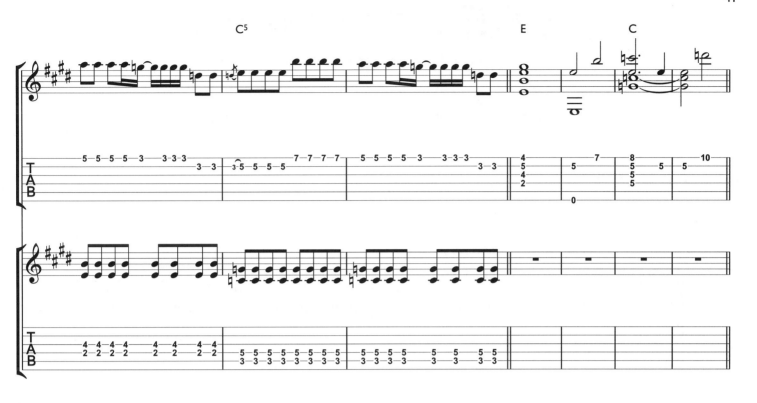

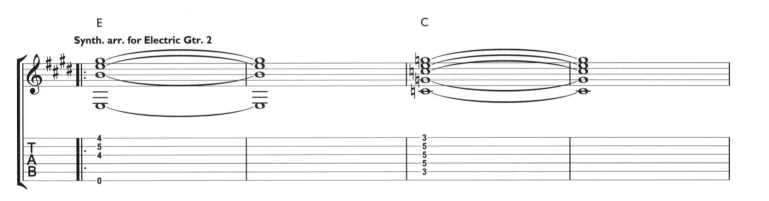

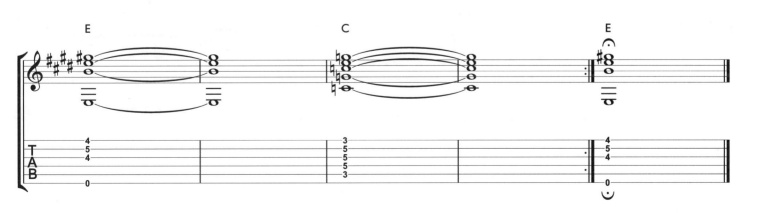

L.S.F. [LOST SOULS FOREVER]

Words and Music by Sergio Pizzorno and Christopher Karloff

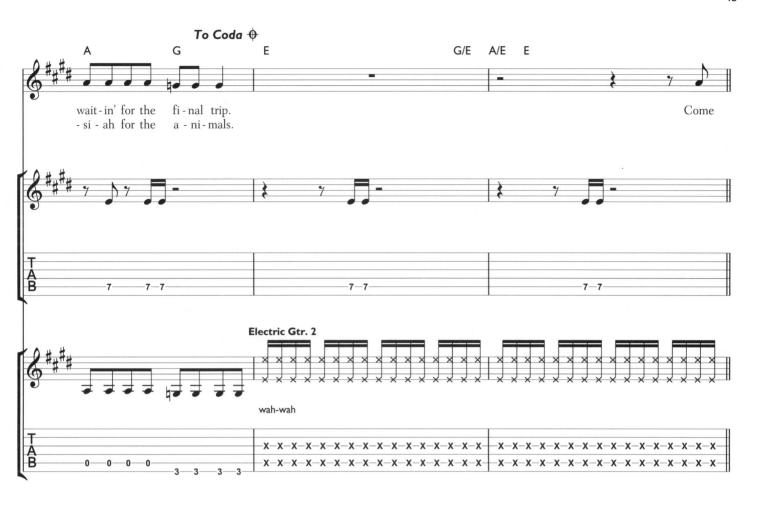

wait-in' for the   fi-nal trip.
-si-ah for the   a-ni-mals.   Come

Electric Gtr. 2

wah-wah

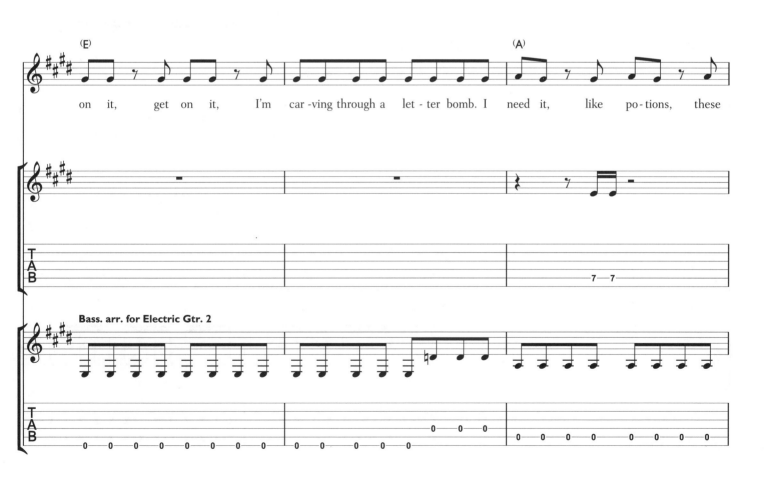

on it,   get on it,   I'm car-ving through a   let-ter bomb. I   need it,   like po-tions,   these

Bass. arr. for Electric Gtr. 2

drugs are just an hour a-way. Come on it, 'lec - tron-ic,   a   po - ly - phon-ic   pros - ti - tute. The

mo tor's   on fi - re,   Mes - si - ah   for the an - i - mals.

(Aah,_____

Electric Gtr. 2

wah-wah

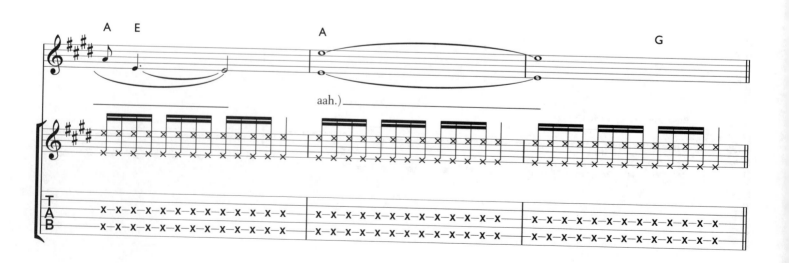

aah.)_____

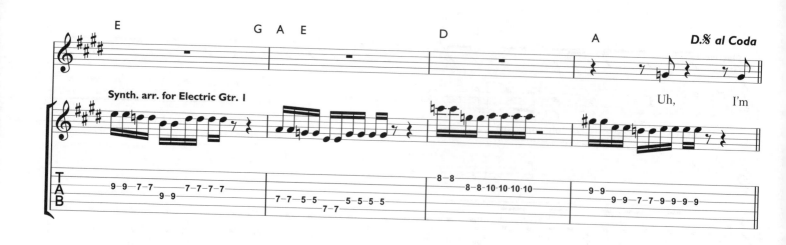

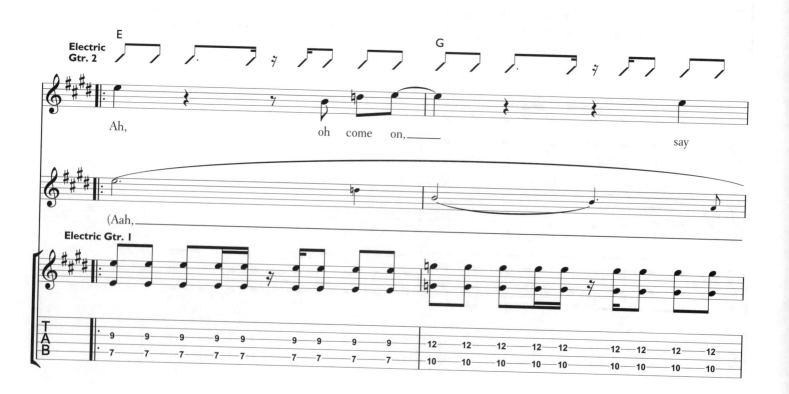

we got our backs to the wall.___ Get on___ and watch out_

(Aah.)___

be-fore you kill us all.___

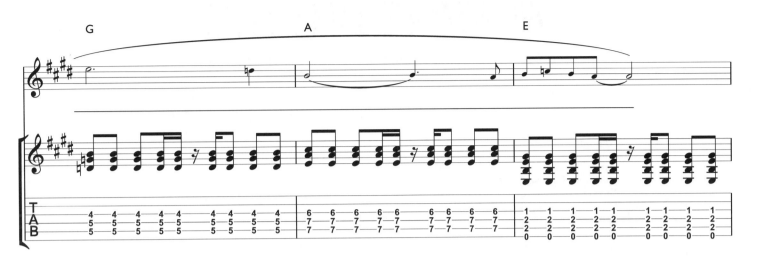

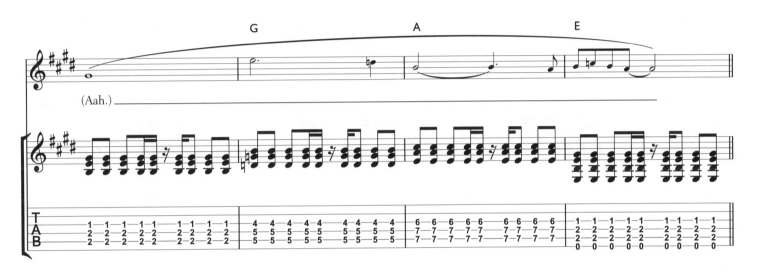

Keyboard arr. for Electric Gtr. I

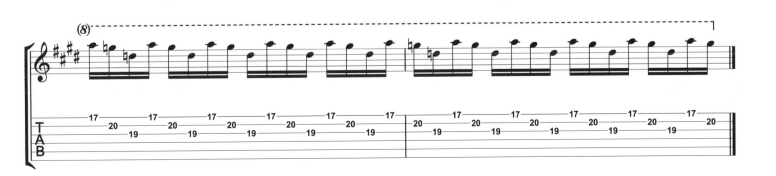

RUNNING BATTLE

Words and Music by Sergio Pizzorno and Christopher Karloff

(1.) I take down what I need,   'cause you know I need to breathe I'm
2. So keep those voi - ces down,   you're_ in view don't make no sound. A

tired of walk - in' on an - oth - er plane,_   an - oth - er plane 'cause I feel in - sane   I...
thou-sand voi - ces mak - in' all the mis - takes.   The fire es - capes_ and this code must break   I...

step back to get___ to you,___ cut-tin' back I'm fall - in' through.

An-oth-er day I feel___ the same,___ I'm cut - ting and I'm bleed - ing here___ with

Synth. arr. for Electric Gtr. 2

let ring

you. All ly - in' a - cross___ the ground___ try - ing hard to make___ no sound___ when

two men gon - na break___ you down I said, two men gon - na break___ you down, I break.

cont. sim.

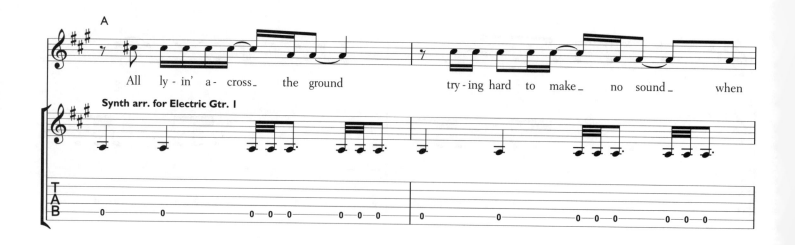

All ly-in' a-cross_ the ground   try-ing hard to make_ no sound_ when

two men gon-na break   you down I said   two men gon-na break_ you down, I break.

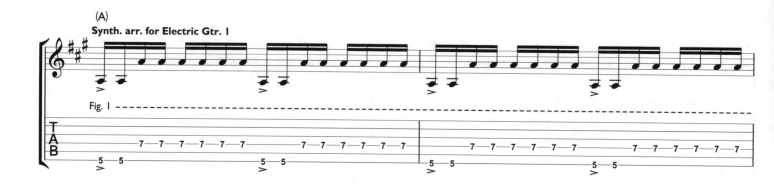

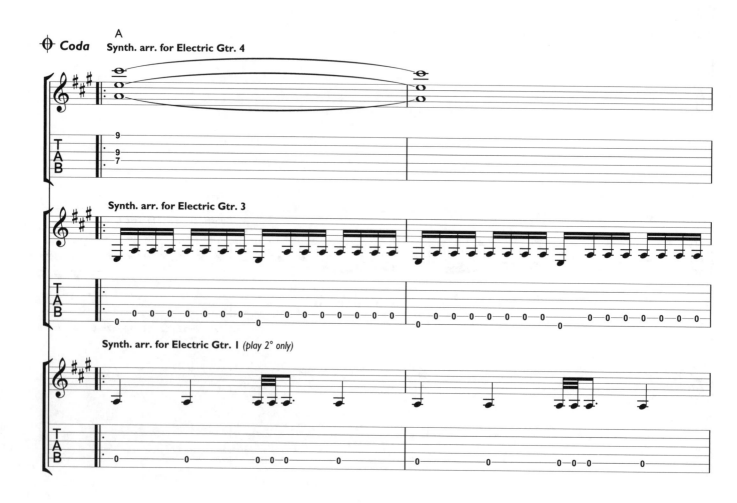

TEST TRANSMISSION

Words and Music by Sergio Pizzorno and Christopher Karloff

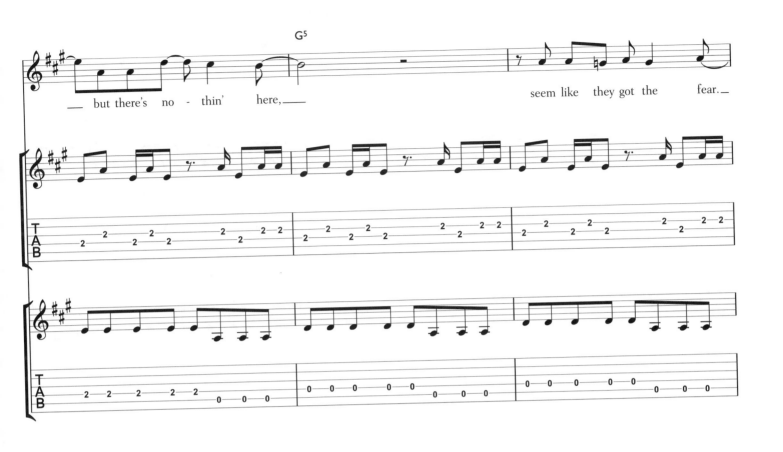

but there's no - thin' here,___ seem like they got the fear.___

Cat-tle grids rat - tle gold___ chains, pay it back,

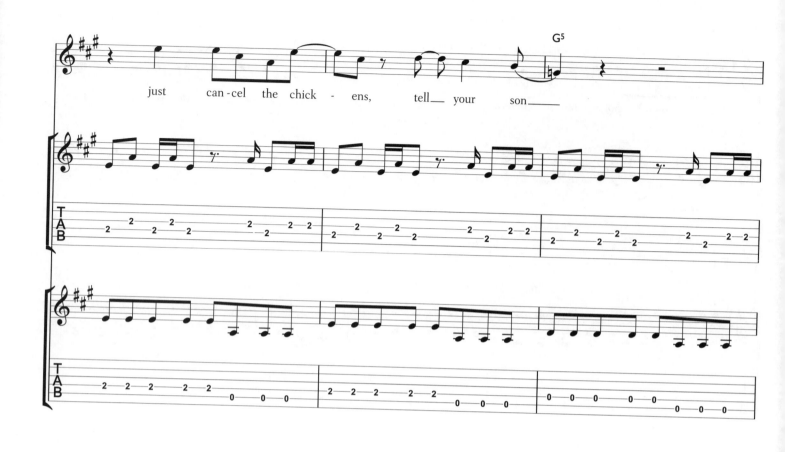

just can -cel the chick - ens, tell__ your son__

that he should steal_ the gold.__

(S. S. S. S. S. S. S. S.)

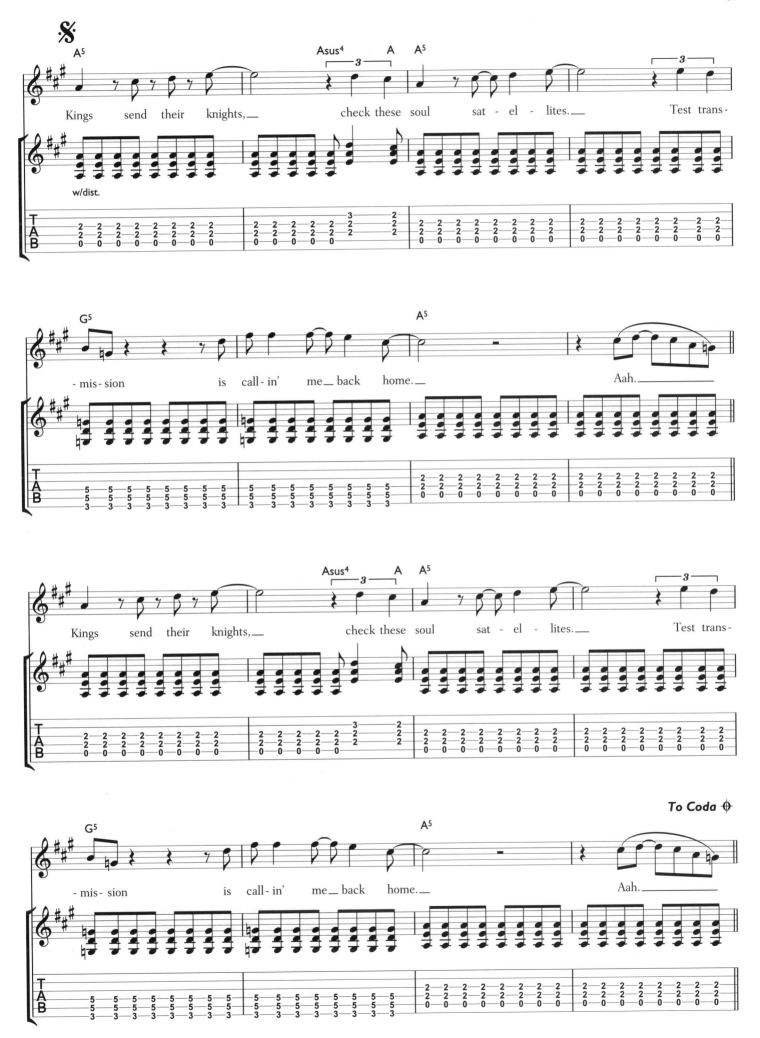

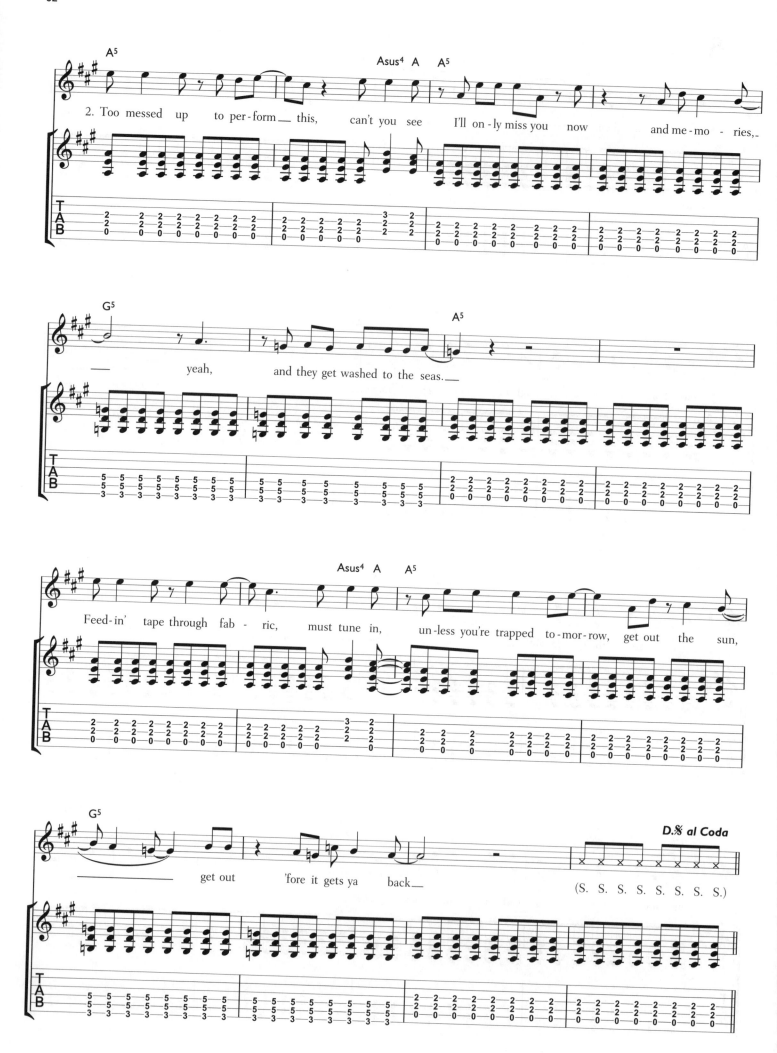

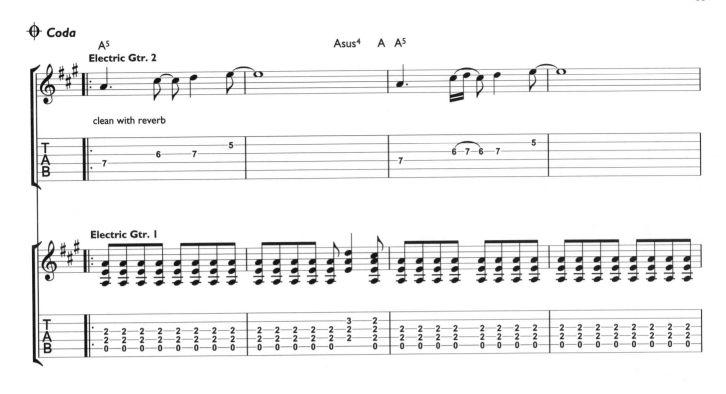

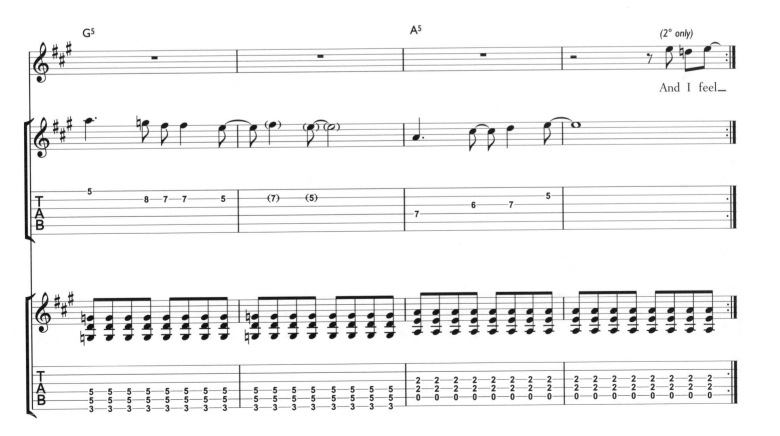

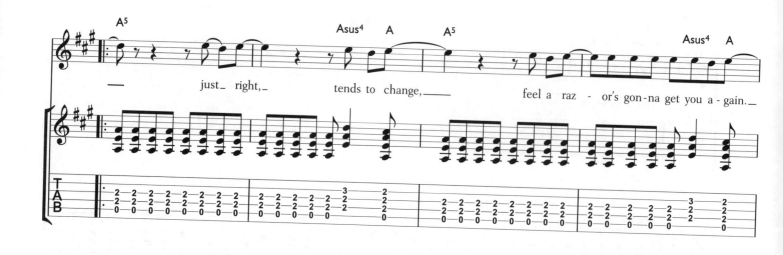

just— right,— tends to change,_____ feel a raz - or's gon-na get you a - gain._

— Set-tin' sun___ is com-in' back a - gain. And I feel

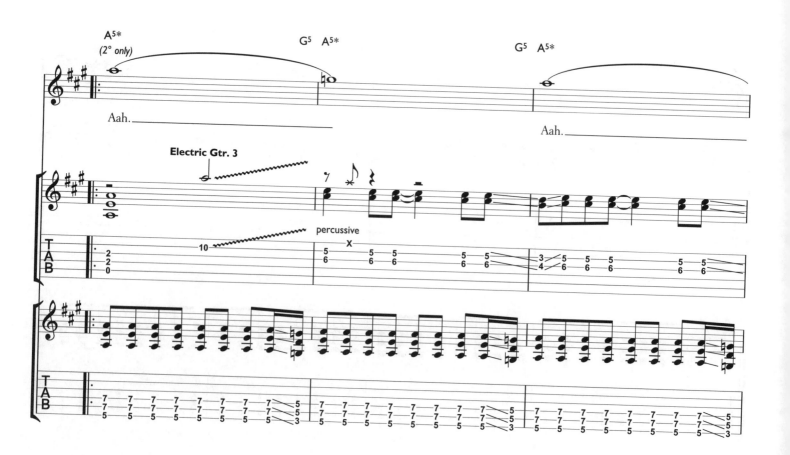

Aah._____ Aah._____

Electric Gtr. 3

percussive

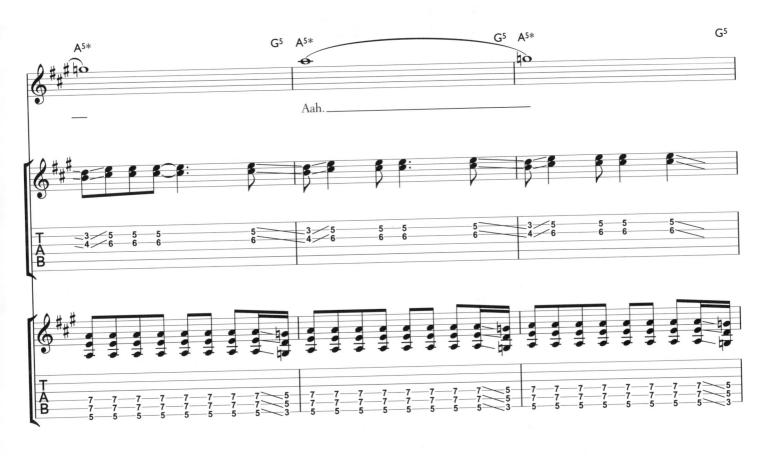

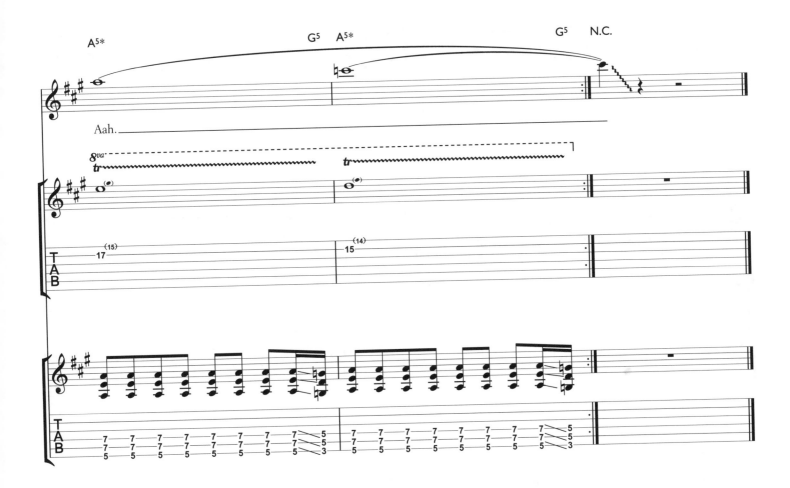

CUTT OFF

Words and Music by Sergio Pizzorno and Christopher Karloff

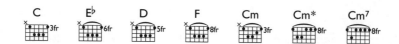

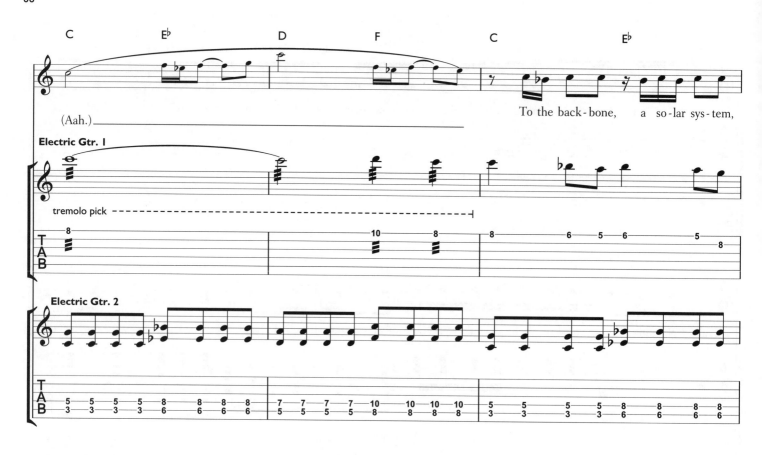

(Aah.)

To the back-bone, a so-lar sys-tem,

Electric Gtr. 1

tremolo pick

Electric Gtr. 2

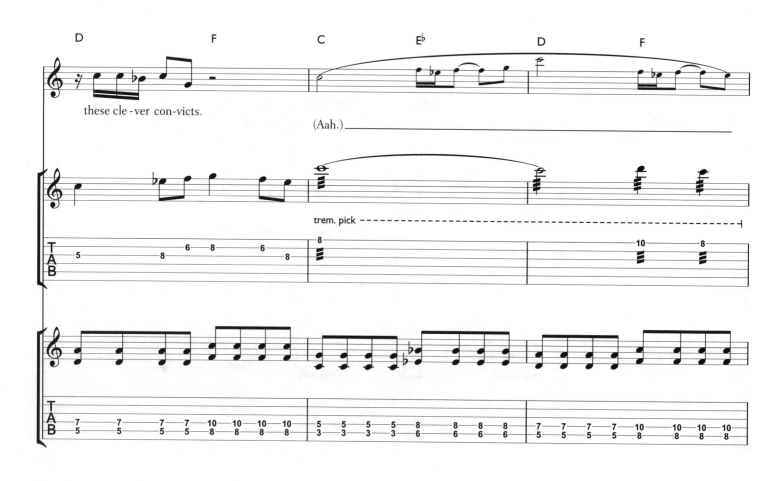

these cle-ver con-victs.

(Aah.)

trem. pick

all those spies and strikes you hear are cling-ing to their guns and

if you smell those al-monds man, I think you bet-ter run check out.

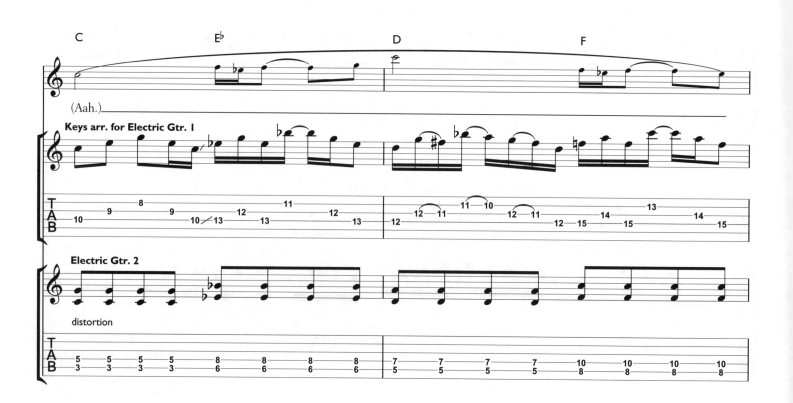

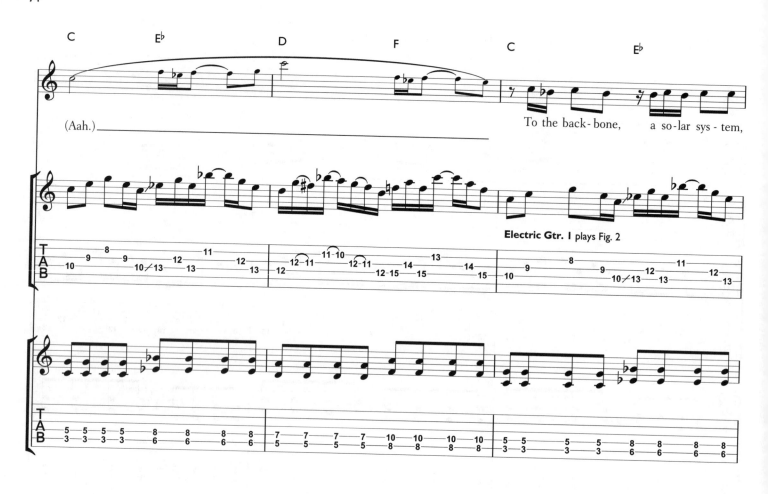

To the back-bone, a so-lar sys-tem, these cle-ver con-victs.

BUTCHER BLUES

Words and Music by Sergio Pizzorno and Christopher Karloff

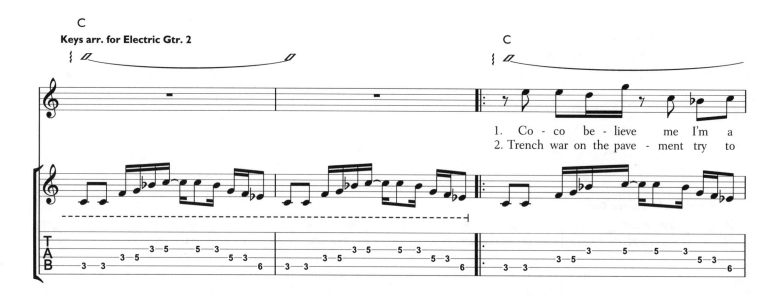

-self un - der - ground.   I said that   you must be - lieve_ me when I say I'm
fa - ces with fiends.   I guess that   you've nev - er been_ here by the

Tacet 1°------------------| Tacet 2°------------------------------------

fight - in' the dead.___   Ly - in' low a - cross_ the eve - nin',   can you see the
look up - on your face   stand - in' with all the whores and can - ni - bals   and the

lumps on my head? }   But I got these voi - ces that just keep sing - in' out   say - in'...
cen - sored race. }

C

C

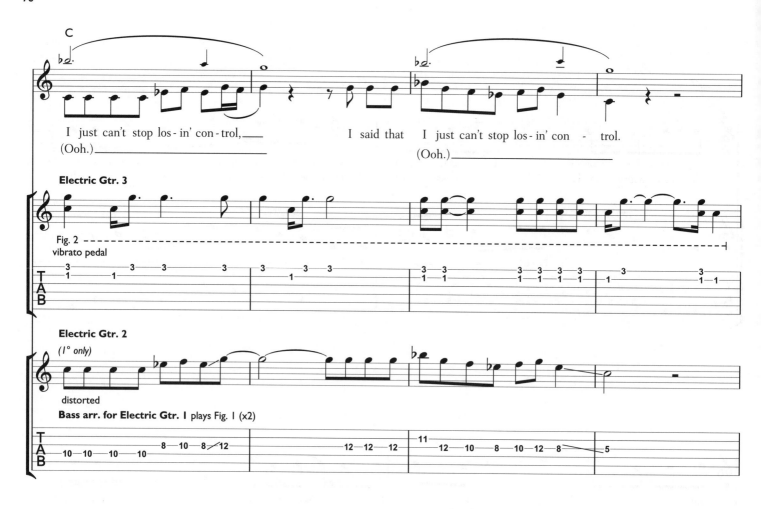

I just can't stop los-in' con-trol,____ I said that I just can't stop los-in' con - trol.
(Ooh.)____ (Ooh.)____

Electric Gtr. 3

Fig. 2 -
vibrato pedal

Electric Gtr. 2

(1° only)

distorted

Bass arr. for Electric Gtr. 1 plays Fig. 1 (x2)

I just can't stop los-in' con-trol,____ I said that I just can't stop los-in' con - trol.
(Ooh.)____ (Ooh.)____

(1° only)

with delay

(play both times)

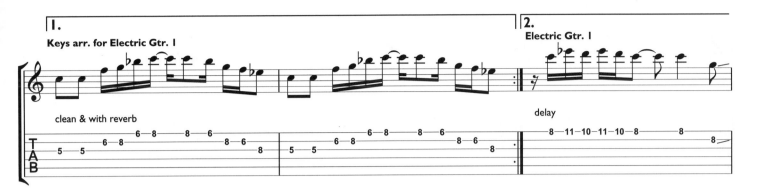

You must be-lieve me when I say I'm fight - ing the dead.__ Ly - in'

Bass arr. for Electric Gtr. I plays Fig. I (x2)

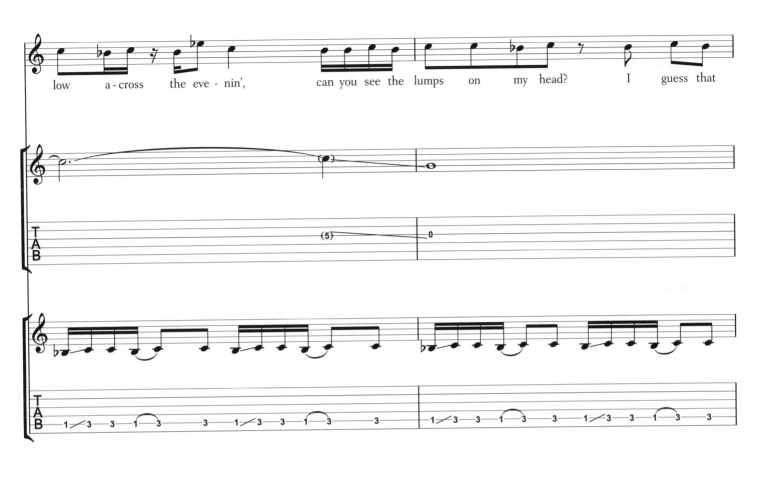

low a-cross the eve-nin', can you see the lumps on my head? I guess that

you've nev-er been here by the look up-on your face. Stand-in' with

all the whores and can-ni-bals and the cen-sored race. Well I got these voi-

-ces that just keep sing-in' out say-in' I just can't stop los-in' con-trol,___
(Ooh)___

Synth. arr. for Electric Gtr. 2

Bass arr. for Electric Gtr. 1

I said that I just can't stop los-in' con -
(Ooh.)

- trol.
I just can't stop los-in' con - trol,___
(Ooh.)
I said that

I just can't stop los - in' con - trol.
(Ooh.)

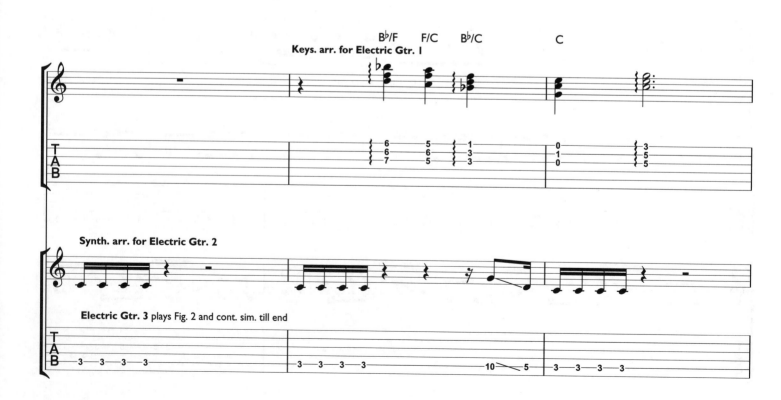

Bb/F   F/C   Bb/C   C

Keys. arr. for Electric Gtr. I

Synth. arr. for Electric Gtr. 2

Electric Gtr. 3 plays Fig. 2 and cont. sim. till end

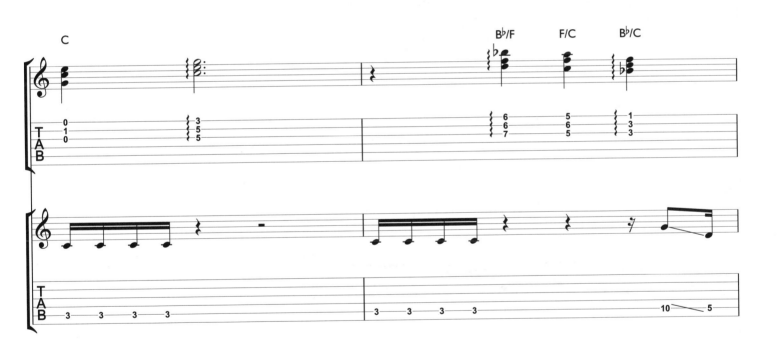

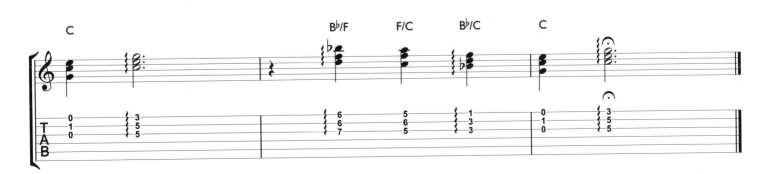

OVARY STRIPE

Words and Music by Sergio Pizzorno and Christopher Karloff

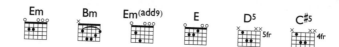

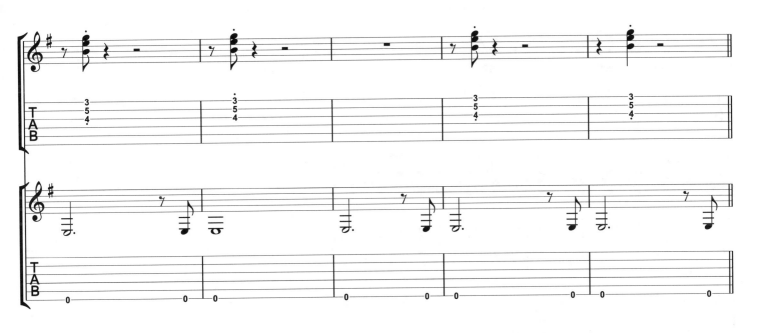

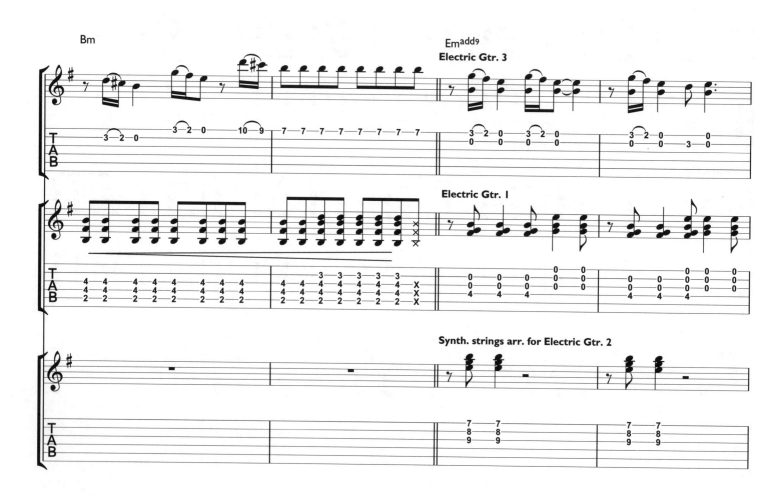

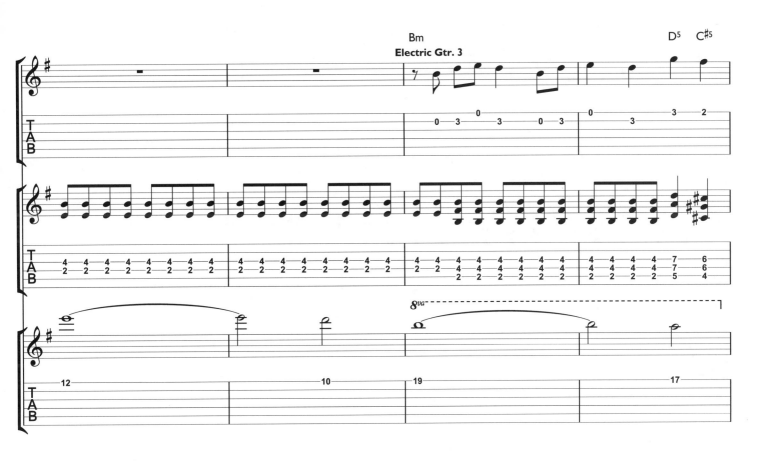

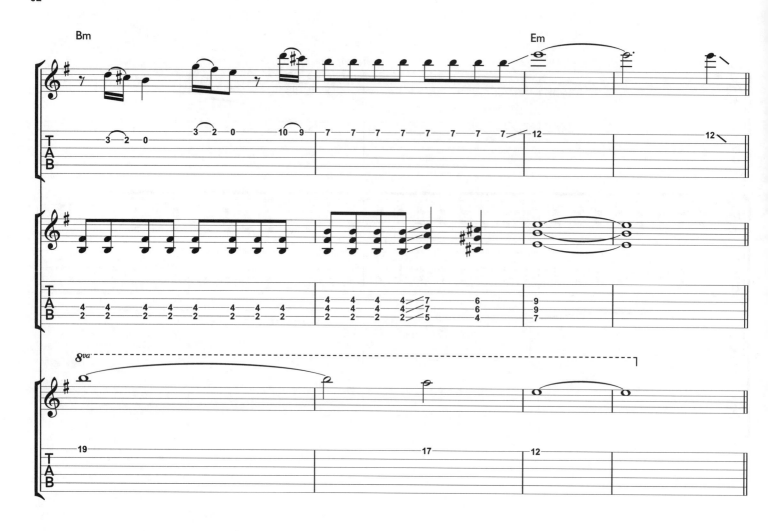

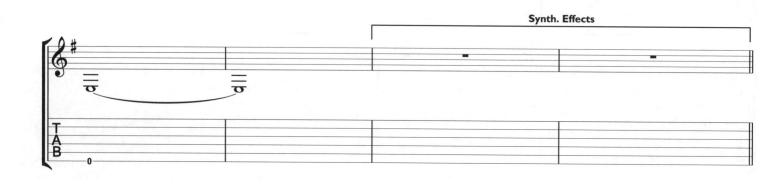

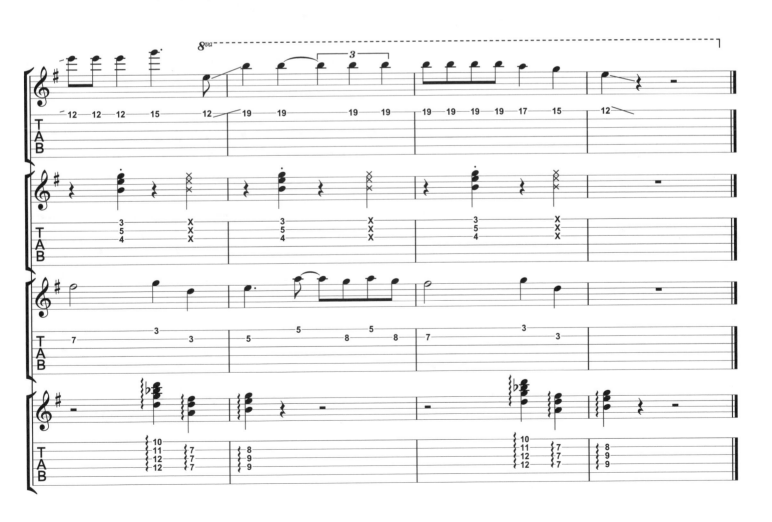

U BOAT

Words and Music by Sergio Pizzorno and Christopher Karloff

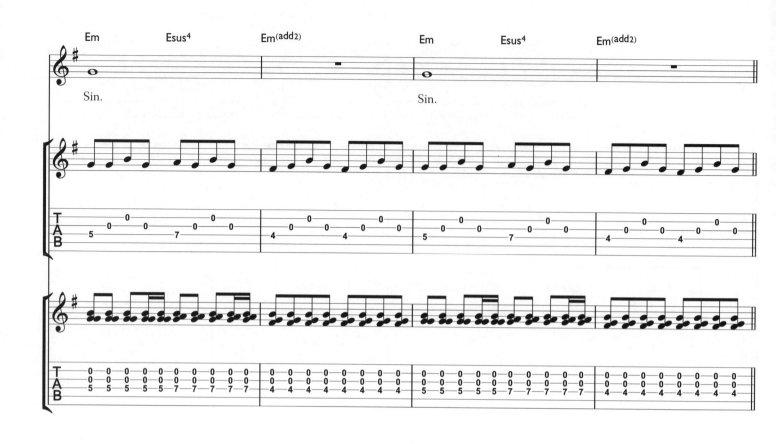

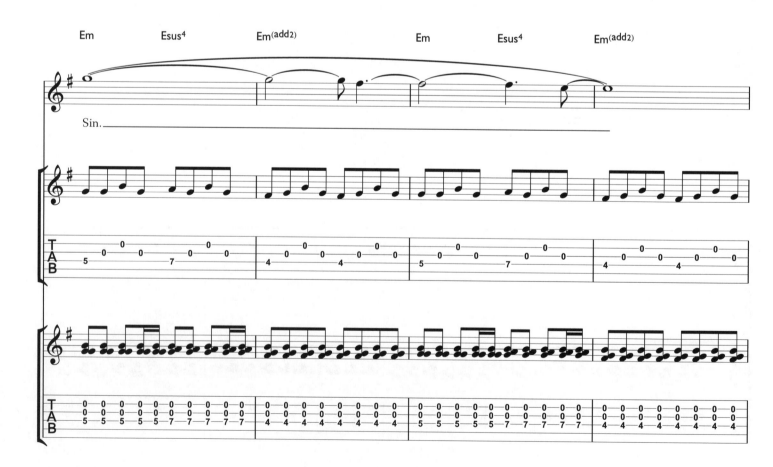

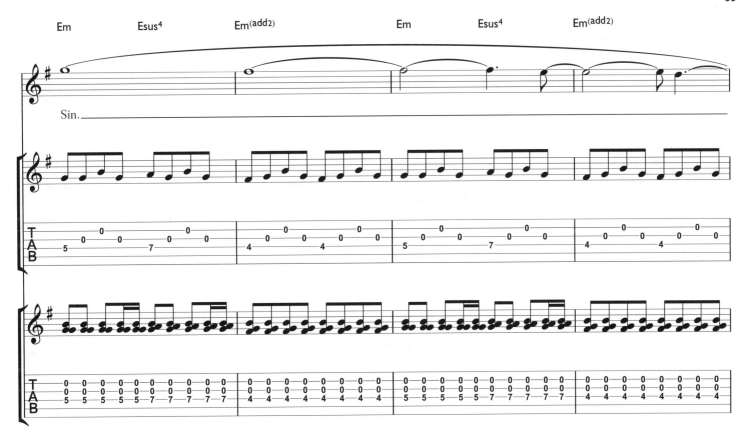

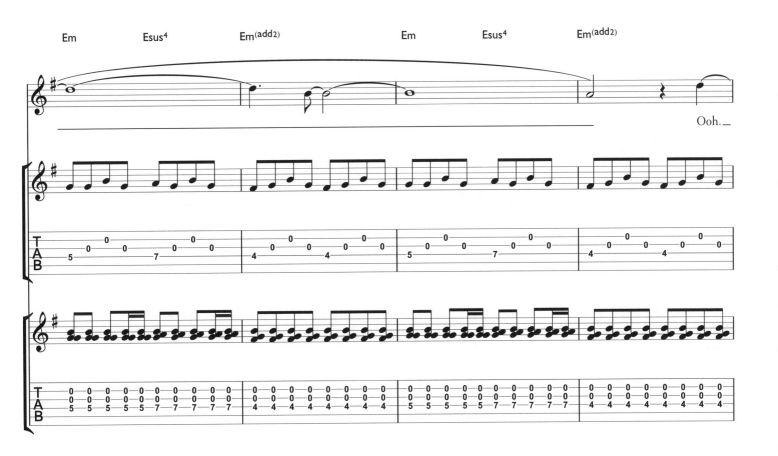

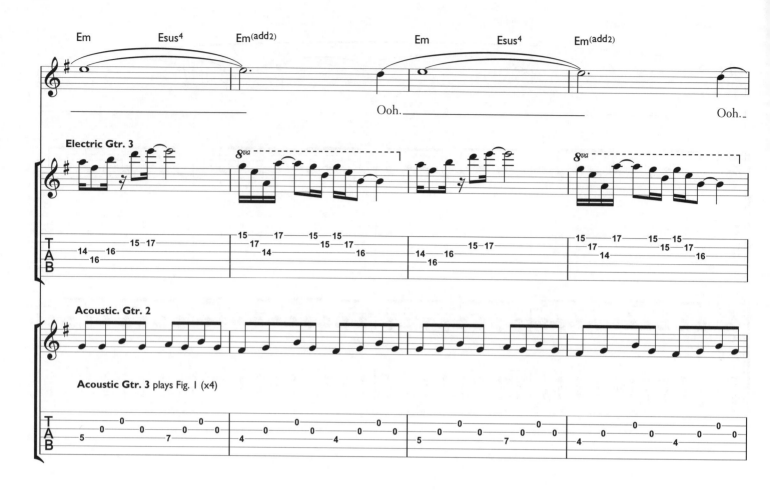

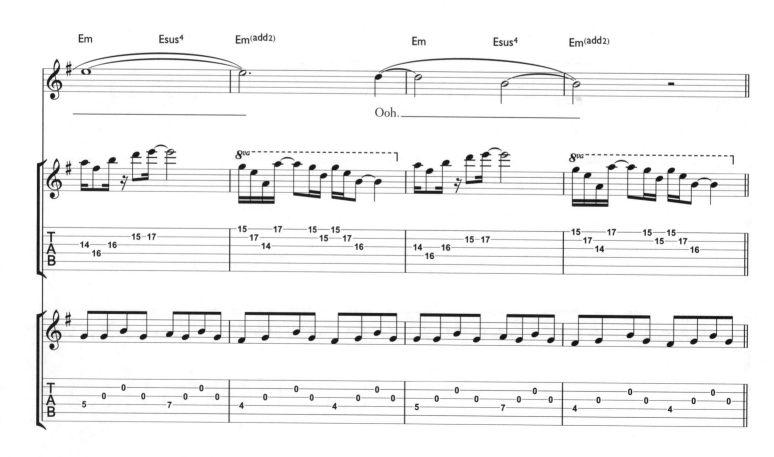

Synth. arr. for Electric Gtr. I

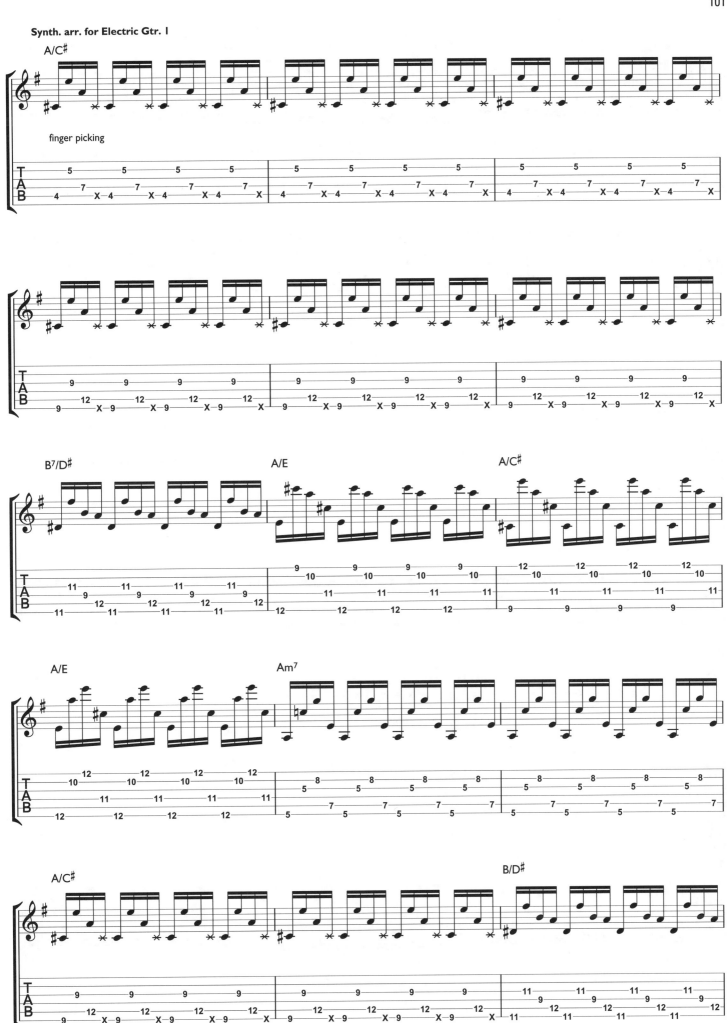

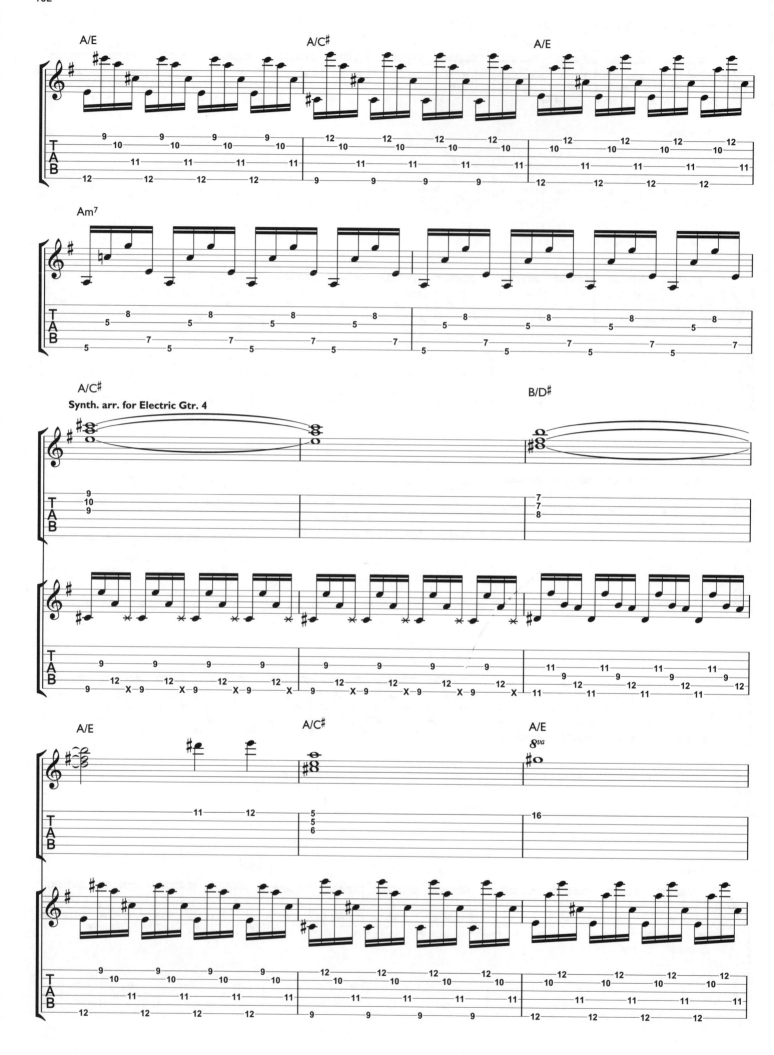

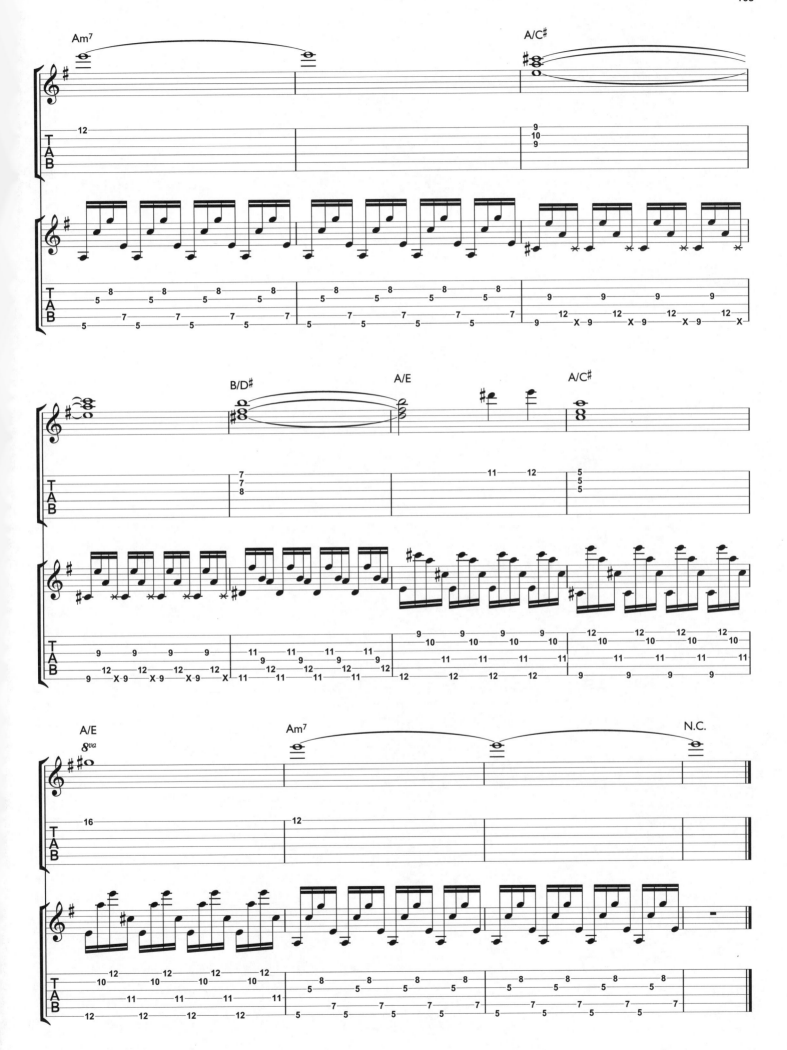